THE SWORD IN THE STONE

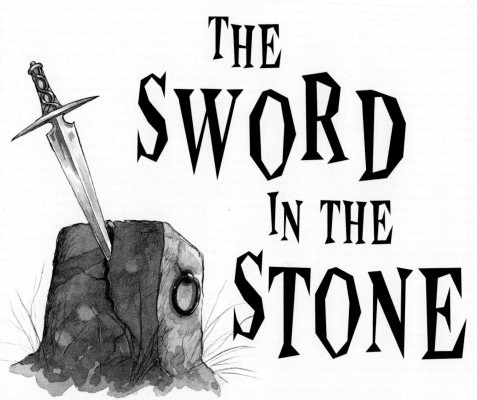

by Jane Langford

Illustrated by David Roberts

CAST

Narrator

②

Archbishop
of London

Merlin
a magician

Sir Ector
father to
Sir Kay and
Arthur

Sir Kay

Arthur

3

SCENE ONE

Outside St Paul's Church, London

Narrator  England has been without a King for thirteen long and troubled years. Since Uther Pendragon died without an heir, the leaderless country has slowly but surely descended into chaos.

Archbishop Tell me Merlin, how shall we determine who is fit to rule our fair country?

Merlin The witch Morgan le Fay has a strong claim …

Archbishop May the Lord protect us!

Merlin … And there are powerful contestants among the knights and barons throughout the land.

Archbishop Quite so! The matter gives rise to constant squabbling! Do you have any advice to offer, wise Merlin?

Merlin I believe the time has arrived for me to exert my magical powers.

4

Archbishop   Your magical powers? Tell me more, Merlin.

Merlin   I have a plan that will help us to find the true King of England. Go, Your Honour, and preach your Christmas service. Then bid the nobles assemble in the church square.

Narrator   *The Archbishop follows Merlin's instructions. After the service, the nobles gather in the church square. A miraculous sight meets their eyes.*

Sir Ector   Look! A sword! Someone has plunged a sword straight into a block of stone!

Archbishop   It's a miracle!

Merlin   *(hisses at Archbishop from behind gravestone)* No, it's not a miracle. It's magic! Read the words on the stone.

Archbishop   Silence, Sires! Listen to the words engraved upon the stone: WHOSOEVER PULLS THIS SWORD FROM THE STONE IS THE TRUE-BORN KING OF ENGLAND.

Sir Ector   The King of England? We have long needed a King. But who would dare put himself forward?

Merlin *(hisses at Archbishop)* It could be Sir Ector. Tell him to make an attempt!

Archbishop Sir Ector, my old friend. Why not make an attempt yourself to pull the sword from the stone?

Sir Ector *(tries and fails)* No ... it will not budge! I'm not the chosen sovereign!

Merlin *(hisses)* Tell the others to try their hand!

Narrator *So the Archbishop invites all the other nobles to try and pull the sword from the stone. One by one they try ... and fail. Their unhappy mutterings fill the church square.*

Sir Ector It appears that no one present is fit for this exalted position.

Merlin *(aside)* That's no surprise to me.

Archbishop Listen, everyone! We will hold a tournament on New Year's Day. Every noble gentleman in the land will be invited. After the festivities we will let them all try to pull this enchanted sword from its shaft of stone.

Sir Ector Then England will have her rightful King! Hooray!

SCENE TWO

London City

Narrator *Sir Ector carries news of the tournament back home to his sons, Kay and Arthur. They are overwhelmed by the excitement and anticipation of such an event. On New Year's Eve they pack their bags and travel to London.*

Sir Kay This will be my first ever tournament since I was made a knight.

Arthur You're fortunate. I would that I were a knight.

Sir Kay Humph! You're far too young!

Arthur I turned sixteen last Whitsun!

Sir Ector Hush, my sons, hush! The streets of London are noisy enough without your empty chattering. Behold the crowds. We must find a place to lodge without delay.

Narrator *A nearby inn has rooms for hire. Sir Ector and his sons stay there for the night, then set off early next morning for the tournament.*

Sir Ector See yonder! The tournament ground, and jousting already under way.

Sir Kay Jousting? I haven't brought my jousting lance. All I have is my sword … my sword! Where **is** my sword?

Arthur It's in your sheath. You put it there this very morning.

Sir Kay Yes, but then I took it out to burnish it further. Oh woe is me! I must have left it at our lodgings!

Sir Ector What! How can you have been so careless?

Sir Kay I'm sorry, Father, I was indeed foolish and forgetful. I was anxious to get to the tournament.

Arthur We will have to go back for it!

Sir Ector There is no time for that! If we go back now we will miss the tournament.

Arthur Don't fret, Father. You proceed. I will return and fetch the sword.

Narrator *So Arthur races back to the inn. But the innkeeper has boarded up the doors and gone to the tournament with his wife. Arthur cannot gain entry to their lodgings.*

Arthur Now how am I to proceed? Kay will not forgive me if I return empty-handed.

Narrator *Arthur plods back through the streets of London. The sun shines brightly on this otherwise gloomy morning. As Arthur passes the church of St Paul's, a glint of metal catches his eye.*

Arthur What is that in the church square? It looks like a sword.

Merlin *(whispers from behind a gravestone)* Of course it's a sword, boy. Go and look!

Arthur Good gracious! It **is** a sword. But why would anyone want to put a sword in a block of stone? I trust the blade is not damaged.

Merlin The blade damaged! Huh! Who does he think I am?

Narrator *Arthur clambers up the side of the stone block and grabs the sword. It slides easily from the granite's grip and Arthur holds it aloft. The sunlight bounces off it like a silver shower.*

Arthur A truly wonderful weapon. Kay should be well satisfied with this!

Merlin *(peeping round gravestone)* I'm certain that he will!

Narrator *Arthur hurries back to the tournament. Kay is waiting anxiously.*

Sir Kay What kept you so long?

Arthur I'm sorry, the inn was bolted up. I've brought you a replacement.

Sir Kay A replacement? Let me see!

Narrator *Sir Kay grabs the sword. He looks at it suspiciously.*

Arthur I found it in the church square, plunged deep in a block of stone. But don't worry, the blade isn't damaged.

Sir Kay *(suspiciously)* In a block of stone?

Arthur Yes.

Sir Kay In the church square?

Arthur Yes. It did not appear to belong to anyone. Honestly!

Narrator *Arthur does not know about the significance of the sword in the stone. But Sir Kay does. He cannot believe his luck. He sends Arthur to get some ale, then he hurries to find his father.*

Sir Kay Father! Father! Look I have the sword.

Sir Ector At last! ... But that is not your sword.

Sir Kay No. It is the sword from the stone.

Sir Ector What? The sword from the stone? How did you come by it?

Sir Kay I simply withdrew it. It was a simple matter. Look, is it not an amazing weapon?

Sir Ector Yes. B-but ... That means ...

Sir Kay Precisely! I'm destined to be King of England!

Sir Ector You? King of England?

Merlin *(aside)* Heaven help us all!

SCENE THREE

St Paul's Church Square

Narrator *Sir Kay and Sir Ector hurry to find the Archbishop and tell him the news. The Archbishop is astonished. He hastily summons all the most important nobles, barons, knights and ladies to meet at the church square. Soon they are assembled.*

Archbishop We must witness this miracle ourselves. Advance, Sir Kay. Show us how you pulled that sword from the very heart of that solid rock.

Sir Kay There's no need for that. I have the sword. Surely that is proof enough?

Sir Ector No, son. It is not. Now put the sword back in the stone so that we may all see you draw it out!

Sir Kay *(struggling with the sword)* But it won't go back in!

Archbishop It won't?

Sir Kay No!

Narrator *While Kay struggles to replace the sword, Arthur runs into the church square carrying a pitcher of ale.*

Arthur There you are! I've been looking everywhere for you. What's going on?

Sir Ector Your brother is trying to replace the sword in the stone.

Arthur Replace it? Oh dear. Was it wrong to remove it? Please don't blame Kay. It was my fault. I took it from the stone.

Sir Ector Pardon? What did you say?

Arthur The sword. I'm sorry. I took it without permission.

Archbishop You took it? But that's impossible! You're only a boy!

Arthur But it was not difficult. Let me show you.

Narrator *Arthur takes the sword from Kay. He clambers onto the stone and slides the sword back into its heart. Gasps from the crowd echo around the church square.*

Arthur Behold. The sword was lodged in the stone like this … And I pulled it out – like this!

Narrator *Arthur holds the sword high for everyone to see. The sun slips from between the clouds, and a shaft of golden beams falls on Arthur and the stone.*

Archbishop A boy? Our King? How can such a thing be?

Arthur A King? I'm no King!

Merlin *(peeping round gravestone)* Yes you are, my boy!

Sir Ector Kay. Is this true? Was it Arthur who pulled the sword from the stone?

Sir Kay *(head hung down with shame)* Yes, Father. Our lodgings were locked, so he took this sword from the church square in its stead.

Sir Ector I see! I understand everything now.

Archbishop Well, I do not! Arthur cannot be crowned King. He is but a youth. He has no royal blood. There must be some mistake!

Sir Ector No. There is no mistake.

Narrator   *Sir Ector takes Arthur to one side. He holds the boy's shoulders and looks sadly into his eyes.*

Sir Ector   Arthur, what I have to tell you now is very difficult for me. I love you as a son, but you are not truly mine. Your real father was Uther Pendragon, King of England.

Arthur   No! I cannot believe this! **You** are my father!

Sir Ector   No. King Uther was your father. When you were born, his enemies were strong and ruthless. Your life was in danger. Uther told Merlin to bring you to me for safe-keeping. I have cared for you since you were a baby. But now you are a man and you need to know the truth.

Merlin   *(stepping out from behind the gravestone)* And now Arthur is King and he needs to rule his country!

SCENE FOUR

At St Paul's Church

Narrator *There is much celebration in London this day. Arthur is carried shoulder high into St Paul's, and immediately made a Knight of the Realm. He is dubbed Sir Arthur with the very same sword that he had plucked from the stone. Three days later he is crowned King of England.*

Merlin Three cheers for Arthur Pendragon, King of England!

Archbishop Three cheers for King Arthur! May his reign be long and just!

17

Arthur My thanks to you, Merlin. And to you, Archbishop. As I stand before you with the crown of England on my head I make three promises: I promise to rule wisely; I promise to do my best to right all wrongs; I promise to bring peace and prosperity to all the land!

Sir Ector *(stepping forward from the crowd)* I am proud of you, my boy.

Arthur Father!

Sir Ector *(sadly shaking head)* No, not Father.

Arthur Yes! **Father!** For you will always be Father to me. Come to court and stay with me. You too, Kay! You will both remain in the service of the King for as long as you wish!

Narrator *Arthur embraced his father and his brother. During his reign as King of England they supported him with their love, the Archbishop supported him with good advice, and Merlin …*
… Well, Merlin did what he always did best – make magic!

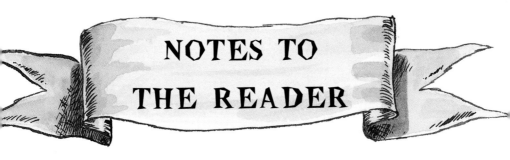

NOTES TO THE READER

Did Arthur exist? No one knows for sure. We do know that the Ancient Britons had to fight off the northern Picts, the Irish, and Saxon invaders. The Britons were led by a chieftain, a hero of his time – could this have been Arthur?

The play in this book is based on one of the legends that grew up around Arthur in the Middle Ages. These legends were written down by medieval writers, who knew how to weave historical facts with tales of chivalry and romance to produce the 'must read' stories of their day!

Arthur

Arthur was brought up by Sir Ector and was unaware that his real father was Uther Pendragon, the last King of England, who died when Arthur was a baby.

Uther had married Igraine. She had three daughters by her first marriage, one of whom was Morgan le Fay, who became Arthur's implacable enemy.

Merlin had predicted that Uther would be killed in battle soon after Arthur's birth. Knowing that Arthur would then be in great danger from his enemies, Uther agreed to entrust his baby to Merlin's care. Merlin found him a secure home with Sir Ector, a knight who had been loyal to Uther.

Merlin

Merlin is a truly magical figure; it is said that he made his first prophecies as a child aged 7! Traditionally seen as a bearded old man dressed in the long flowing robes of a magician, he is a time-traveller and shape-shifter and appears from nowhere to help Arthur at critical moments. He is Arthur's protector, friend and guide. He arranges the 'sword in the stone' contest which leads to Arthur becoming King.

What next?

As well as *The Sword in the Stone*, there are two other Navigator plays dealing with King Arthur's early years; *Excalibur* and *The Scheming of Morgan le Fay*. Other stories recount his marriage to Guinevere, and his various adventures alongside his fellow Knights of the Round Table, among them Lancelot, Gawain and Galahad.

It is said that Arthur didn't die at Avalon, but that he lies with his knights in a deep sleep underground ready to come to the rescue again in a time of crisis. Authors continue to write about these mysterious heroes. *The Once and Future King* is a famous book by T. E. White, which tells the story of Arthur's boyhood in a way that is as funny as it is poignant. This is a good place to start if you want to know more. Kevin Crossley-Holland's *Arthur* trilogy is a more recent exploration of Arthurian legends.

READY, STEADY, ACT!

Now that you have read this play, why not perform it for an audience? It happens on New Year's Eve, a very long time ago. You will need to create a magical atmosphere …

CHOOSING THE PARTS

Choose who will play each part. Hold an audition for the six roles.

- The narrator is a clear speaker who talks directly to the audience. The style of the language is poetic.
- The Archbishop of London is a melodramatic character. His responses are exaggerated.
- Merlin is a powerful magician. He adds magic to the play.
- Sir Ector is a kindly man who loves Arthur as his son.
- Sir Kay is an arrogant young knight who gets shown up.
- Arthur is a likeable teenager who is keen to help.

Who in your cast would be best at these roles? Choose some typical lines from each character and test them out. It will not matter if girls play some of the male parts.

SETTING THE SCENE

There are four scenes in two locations in this play – in a churchyard and in the City of London. The play is set in medieval times.

Decide how you will show your audience where they are. You could use banners, lighting and music. You could even give the narrator some extra lines.

You might want to write and publish a programme for the audience to give them the historical background to the play. You could use the 'Notes to the Reader' for ideas.

If possible, play some suitable music and take turns to cross the performance space as medieval Londoners, on your own and in pairs. You could be street sellers, an urchin who has stolen an apple, a knight returning from the war, a blacksmith on his way to the forge, a town crier, or a beggar.

Did you know...?
Did you know that actors learn falling and sword-fighting at drama school?

WHAT YOU WILL NEED

Costumes

Tales of King Arthur are often enacted in medieval costumes. This story, which happens in London in the New Year, has more ordinary people than usual. You can give a medieval effect with lots of trailing drapery and strange headgear! You could make some armour, using the pictures in the book to help.

Props

Make a props list using the text.

The biggest challenge is the sword in the stone. You could use a bucket full of sand covered with a scrunched up grey or brown cloth to look like stone. You could then stick in a toy sword or one that you have made. Don't forget to stick some jewels on the hilt.

Sound effects

It would be great to have something special happen when Arthur removes the sword. Use instruments to make a magical sound and maybe sprinkle some glitter or confetti.

SPEAKING AND MOVING

Speaking

There are several different styles of speaking in this play. The Narrator knows the story so he or she speaks with confidence and foresight. Merlin is a very old but wise Wizard. How could you make his voice sound different from the mortals in the play?

Moving

Where will you position your Narrator? They could stand still or they could move towards the audience while speaking. What will the other actors do while the Narrator is speaking?

How an actor moves should reflect their age, personality and how they are feeling – use your whole bodies and faces to show this as you perform.

Think about how you will give your audience a signal that the play has finished and it is time to applaud!

What next?

When you have performed this play, you might want to:

- Do some research about young Arthur's story and improvise some additional scenes.